Them

M000206907

HOUGHTON MIFFLIN
Reading

Down on the Farm

 HOUGHTON MIFFLIN   BOSTON

Printed in the U.S.A.

ISBN: 0-618-16194-5

6789-BS-06 05 04 03

Design, Art Management, and Page Production: Studio Goodwin Sturges

Contents

Dot Got a Big Pot

by Ann Spivey

illustrated by Ashley Wolff

Dot got a big, big, big pot.
Dot got  .

Dot got ![carrots] .
Dot got ![potatoes] .

3

Dot got  .
Dot got a lot!

Nan, Nat, and Dot sat.
"Is it hot, hot, hot?" said Dot.

"It is hot, hot, hot!" said Nan.
"I like it hot, hot, hot!" said Nat.

Dot sat.

Nan sat.

Nat sat.

The Big, Big Box

by Ann Spivey

illustrated by Gavin Bishop

It is a big, big, big box!
"It is my big, big, big box,"
said Fan Fox.

"It is not," said Dan Cat.
"It is **my** big, big, big box!"

Fan bit it.
Dan hit it.

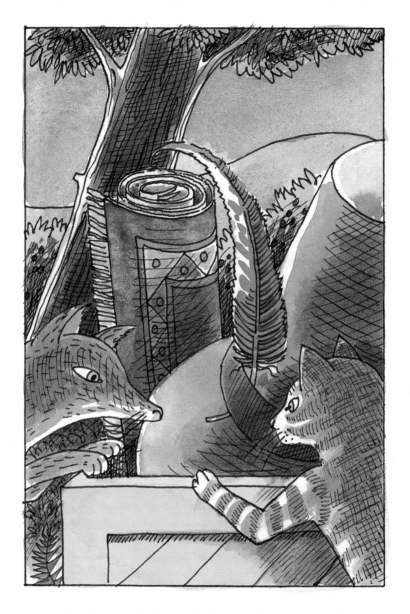

It is a big, big, big mat!
It is a big, big, big hat!

Can it fit?
Can it fit?

14

Fan sat.

Dan sat.

A Pot For Dan Cat

by Ann Spivey
illustrated by Gavin Bishop

"I can see Dan Cat,"
said Fan Fox.

Fan Fox ran.
Dan Cat ran.

Dan Cat can see a big, big pot.
Can Dan Cat fit?

Dan Cat can fit!
Fan Fox ran and ran.

Dan Cat sat.

Word List

Dot Got a Big Pot
DECODABLE WORDS

Target Skill
Short *o*:
Dot, got, hot, lot, pot

Words Using Previously Taught Skills
big, Dot, got, hot, it, lot, Nan, Nat, pot, sat

HIGH-FREQUENCY WORDS

New
said

Previously Taught
a, and, I, is, like

The Big, Big Box
DECODABLE WORDS

Target Skill
Consonant *x*:
box, Fox, ox

Words Using Previously Taught Skills
big, bit, box, can, Cat, Dan, Fan, fit, Fox, hat, hit, it, mat, not, ox, sat

HIGH-FREQUENCY WORDS

New
the

Previously Taught
a, is, my, said

Theme 8, Week 3
A Pot for Dan Cat

DECODABLE WORDS

Words Using Previously Taught Skills
big, can, Cat, Dan, Fan, fit, Fox, pot, ran, sat

HIGH-FREQUENCY WORDS

Previously Taught
a, and, for, I, said, see

HIGH-FREQUENCY WORDS TAUGHT TO DATE

a	have	like	the
and	here	my	to
for	I	said	
go	is	see	

Decoding Skills Taught to Date Consonant *b*, consonant *c*, consonant *d*, consonant *f*, consonant *g*, consonant *h*, consonant *k*, consonant *l*, consonant *m*, consonant *n*, consonant *q*, consonant *r*, consonant *s*, consonant *t*, consonant *v*, consonant *x*, consonant *z*, short *a*, short *i*, short *o*